Deepak Chopra MD

What Are You Hungry For?

Workbook

Before You Begin: Encouraging Words

Hopefully the ideas you've found in *What Are You Hungry For?* have inspired you to try a new approach to reaching your ideal weight. A door has been opened, and you can see that you no longer have to struggle to reach your goal. I personally tested every aspect of the Chopra Solution on myself, and after losing twenty pounds in a short time, I want you to feel encouraged for yourself – this is a satisfying project that brings a deep sense of satisfaction.

Now a journey awaits you. It's nice to have a traveling companion when you undertake any journey. This workbook is going to be your companion. In it you will share your daily experiences as you move from where you are now to where you want to be.

As you've no doubt experienced, dieting is lonely. You are going to throw out all the things that make dieting so futile – the deprivation, the setbacks, the hype that never comes true. Nothing about the journey ahead will resemble being on a diet. But there is still the possibility of feeling lonely, and that's why a workbook is so helpful. You will be able to speak to yourself, share your thoughts day by day, and engage actively in every step of your progress. Your life is your story. You are the author. If you are self-aware, nothing is more fascinating than to create changes in your story, and as you do, your body will follow – in this way, you are activating a new sense of self.

Using the workbook

Familiarize yourself with the layout first. The workbook is divided into themes. Each theme is briefly explained. There are blank pages for you to write in. As these pages get filled, you can easily substitute a spiral notebook or journal with the appropriate headings.

Your assignment is to make a comment on at least one theme a day.

You can pick any theme that seems relevant for that day. If you get inspired you can write on more than one theme a day. But the essential point is this: Don't let a day go by without giving yourself an encouraging word. The purpose of *What Are You Hungry For?* is to change your story, and that happens only when the following conditions are met:

1. You have an intention to grow and evolve.

2. You pay attention to positive changes, even small ones.

3. You send a message to yourself when something good happens – this gives your brain the right new input.

4. You value every change that moves in the direction you desire.

Let's look at a few examples. One theme is "I Ate Better Today." If you have the intention to eat better, you might order an organic salad for lunch. Instead of gobbling down the salad, you ate it carefully, with appreciation for how good it tasted. Afterward, you tuned in and discovered that you weren't hungry anymore, so you skipped dessert. All of these points should be listed in the workbook – they are signs of a small victory, and you will reach your goal through a string of small victories, which in turn will make your brain expect you to be victorious.

Compare this to someone who rushes off to lunch, eats a salad while talking half the time on her mobile phone, and hurries back to work without a second thought about what she ate for lunch. The calories are the same, but in this case there is no intention, no victory, and no self-awareness. Those absent things make all the difference. Plug your brain into your meal, and instead of eating being about calories, it's about you and your story as both evolve and expand.

Take another theme, "I Improved My Self-Image." This is a bit subtler than "I Ate Better Today," but the process is the same. Let's say that a friend compliments you on how good you look – they might comment on your clothes or your mood or your physical appearance. Overweight people, like self-conscious people in general, brush away compliments. Why? Because they don't accept them, and this non-acceptance comes down to self-judgment. The compliment doesn't match their own bad self-image. The inner logic goes something like this: "I don't deserve a compliment, so if I brush off anyone who says something nice about me, I won't have to look at how bad I feel."

You can see, I'm sure, how self-defeating that logic is. So substitute a new logic: "I got a compliment today, which means that my self-image has a reason to improve." Again it's a matter of small victories. Write down in the workbook what the compliment was and add a positive comment about what it felt like to accept the compliment and be pleased by it. See how different this process is, from your brain's viewpoint? You are giving it positive input.

Name Your Feelings

As you write down your daily victories, you will also be asked how you feel about them. Naturally you will feel good, but by using more specific words, you will be sending precise signals to your brain. *What Are You Hungry For?* is all about eating when you are hungry for food instead of eating for emotional reasons. Many overeaters can't name their emotions very well. They feel vaguely "wrong" inside, which causes them to reach for food as a surrogate for finding better emotions.

When you experience a small daily victory, you will be finding those better emotions, so it's good to recognize what they are. When you name something, you can own it. Here's a list of positive feelings to help you on your way:

Proud

Satisfied

Enthusiastic

Joyful

Inspired

Confident

Self-assured

Self-reliant

Creative

Strong

Safe

Successful

Exuberant

Victorious

Healthy

Loving

Refer to this list at the beginning when you are first writing down how you feel about achieving a daily victory – of course, you can use more than one adjective, and feel free to add to the list. The vocabulary of human feelings is rich and practically endless.

The Chopra Solution only asks for one thing, that you nurture your brain through as much positive input as possible, the positivity should be realistic, and it should fit your goals. I'm not asking you to paint a rosy picture all the time. Life has many challenges, and some involve negative things: setbacks, worry, frustration, resistance, and various kinds of obstacles. If you have experienced such things in your desire to lose weight, you know a lot about negative feedback. It might seem that being overweight means, in your eyes, that you deserve negative feedback.

Banish such thoughts from your mind. You are the author of your own story. It's just as easy to focus on the positive aspects as on the negative. If the negative has worn a groove in your mind, that says nothing about what you deserve. From this moment on, your project is to create new pathways in your brain, better habits, greater fulfillment, and a higher vision of life. These things are under your control. You will prove it to yourself by using this workbook. Each theme will prompt you to really appreciate what it means to win personal victories and to build upon theme.

That's the golden road to success. I've offered you an encouraging word. Now let's see all the encouraging words you will offer to yourself.

Workbook Themes

Food and Eating

Your Feelings

Your Lifestyle

Your Inner Growth

1

Food and Eating

"I Ate Better Today"

"I Resisted My Food Triggers"

"I Only Ate When I Was Hungry"

"I Loved What I Was Eating, Without Guilt"

"I Was in Control of My Eating"

"I Ate Better Today"

Your body functions best on natural, fresh, unprocessed food, preferably organic. If you take a step in this direction, enter a comment below and say how this change made you feel.

Eating better also includes your improved behavior: not snacking, not giving in to cravings, and being aware of how much you eat.

The final judgment is yours. If you think you're eating better today, enter a positive word of encouragement.

1. What I did today: _____

_____

_____

How it made me feel: _____

_____

_____

2. What I did today: _____

_____

_____

How it made me feel: _____

_____

_____

3. What I did today: _____

_____

_____

How it made me feel: _____

_____

_____

4. What I did today: _____

_____

_____

How it made me feel: _____

_____

_____

5. What I did today: _____

_____

_____

How it made me feel: _____

_____

_____

6. What I did today: _____

_____

_____

How it made me feel: _____

_____

_____

"I Resisted My Food Triggers"

Triggers are automatic prompts. They make you turn to food without noticing what you're doing. Strong triggers are usually emotional – feeling depressed, anxious, or lonely is enough to trigger your desire to eat. But even when they aren't emotional, triggers are based on habit.

Write down your victory over a food trigger. The whole subject of unconscious eating is covered in the book, but to help you, here's a reminder of the main triggers that make overeaters turn to food. The triggers are divided into Group A and Group B, as in the book, to signify the easier and harder triggers to overcome. That's because it's tough to overcome emotional eating compared to eating that is the result of external circumstances. You don't have to pay special attention to that today – just write down your success at resisting any of your triggers.

Group A (Circumstances): *I will tend to overeat if*

I'm busy or distracted at work.

I'm rushed and on the go.

I'm tired. I haven't had enough sleep.

I'm with other people who are eating.

I'm out at a restaurant.

I'm in front of the TV or computer and need something to do with my hands.

I have a plate of food in front of me, and I feel I must clean my plate.

Group B (Emotions): *I will tend to overeat if*

I'm depressed.

I'm lonely.

I'm feeling unattractive.

I'm feeling anxious or worried.

I'm having negative thoughts about my body.

I'm under stress.

I want to be comforted.

1. What I did today: _____

_____

_____

How it made me feel: _____

_____

_____

2. What I did today: _____

_____

_____

How it made me feel: _____

_____

_____

3. What I did today: _____

_____

_____

How it made me feel: _____

_____

_____

4. What I did today: _____

_____

_____

How it made me feel: _____

_____

_____

5. What I did today: _____

_____

_____

How it made me feel: _____

_____

_____

6. What I did today: _____

_____

_____

How it made me feel: _____

_____

_____

_____

"I Only Ate When I Was Hungry"

What Are You Hungry For? asks for you to be aware of your feelings any time you reach for food, so that you won't use eating as a substitute for your emotional hunger. At the same time, you are asked to judge your actual hunger level, so that you don't automatically eat the same amount every time food is in front of you. These topics are covered in the book.

Write down any victory where you ate purely because you felt hungry, with no ulterior motive and no sense of emotional neediness.

1. What I did today: _____

_____

_____

How it made me feel: _____

_____

_____

_____

2. What I did today: _____

_____

_____

How it made me feel: _____

_____

_____

_____

3. What I did today: _____

_____

_____

How it made me feel: _____

_____

_____

4. What I did today: _____

_____

_____

How it made me feel: _____

_____

_____

5. What I did today: _____

_____

_____

How it made me feel: _____

_____

_____

6. What I did today: _____

_____

_____

How it made me feel: _____

_____

_____

"I Loved What I Was Eating, Without Guilt"

Food is one of life's great joys, and it shouldn't be clouded by the guilt trips that overeaters impose on themselves. Deprivation combined with guilt has ruined the good intentions of millions of dieters.

Write down your victory in finding the pure joy of eating, when there wasn't the shadow of guilt about your enjoyment, either before, during, or after.

1. What I did today: _____

_____

_____

How it made me feel: _____

_____

_____

2. What I did today: _____

_____

_____

How it made me feel: _____

_____

_____

3. What I did today: _____

_____

_____

How it made me feel: _____

_____

_____

4. What I did today: _____

_____

_____

How it made me feel: _____

_____

_____

5. What I did today: _____

_____

_____

How it made me feel: _____

_____

_____

6. What I did today: _____

_____

_____

How it made me feel: _____

_____

_____

"I Was in Control of My Eating"

Most overeaters lose control because they tried to impose it in the first place. Discipline always leads to forcing, and in time it breaks down. This decline is natural; it happens to all of us. But your body already knows how to control your appetite, using hormonal signals for hunger and satiation. Natural control doesn't need to be forced.

Write down any victory where you listened to your body's natural signals and felt in control of your eating. Being in control has the following signs:

Eating just enough to feel satisfied but not so much that you are stuffed.

Not having to clean your plate.

Not automatically needing dessert.

Skipping snacks.

Not feeling victimized by cravings.

Eating without guilt and anxiety.

Picking nutritious food over fast food.

Any step you took today to favor at least one of these things deserves to be noted.

1. What I did today: _____

_____

_____

How it made me feel: _____

_____

_____

2. What I did today: _____

_____

_____

How it made me feel: _____

_____

_____

3. What I did today: _____

_____

_____

How it made me feel: _____

_____

_____

4. What I did today: _____

_____

_____

How it made me feel: _____

_____

_____

5. What I did today: _____

_____

_____

How it made me feel: _____

_____

_____

6. What I did today: _____

_____

_____

How it made me feel: _____

_____

_____

_____

2

Your Feelings

"I Improved My Self-Image"

"I Felt Valued and Appreciated"

"I Felt Good About My Body"

"I Didn't Substitute Food for Feelings"

"I Improved My Self-Image"

When you're overweight, it's easy to fixate on your body image and forget that what comes first is self-image. When you improve your self-image, you gain the confidence to rewrite your life story along the lines you want. Reaching your ideal weight will naturally be part of rewriting your story, but even if your main focus is entirely on self-image, your body will follow suit. That's the secret of weight loss without dieting – using expanded awareness for personal growth.

Write down any victory where your sense of self improved. Use your own standards, but in general a good self-image means the following:

> You stand up for what you believe.
>
> You're confident in who you are.
>
> You feel self-reliant and strong.
>
> You value your independence.
>
> You speak your truth.
>
> You feel comfortable in our own skin.
>
> You are free of shame and guilt.
>
> You feel centered.

Any step you took today to increase at least one of these things deserves to be noted.

1. What I did today: _____

_____

_____

How it made me feel: _____

_____

_____

2. What I did today: _____

_____

_____

How it made me feel: _____

_____

_____

3. What I did today: _____

_____

_____

How it made me feel: _____

_____

_____

4. What I did today: _____

_____

_____

How it made me feel: _____

_____

_____

5. What I did today: _____

_____

_____

How it made me feel: _____

_____

_____

6. What I did today: _____

_____

_____

How it made me feel: _____

_____

_____

"I Felt Valued and Appreciated"

There's a familiar chain of events where somebody overeats because they feel restless and vaguely "off," a feeling that can be traced to living without much meaning, and this in turn goes back to feeling unappreciated and without value in the eyes of other people. So feeling valued and appreciated removes a deep-seated incentive that makes you reach for food in order to feel better.

Write down any incident where someone paid you a compliment, praised your work, or in some way made you feel more valued. It may also be that without anyone saying so, you realized how valuable and appreciated you are. Be your own judge. Each of us must use our own awareness to see the value that's inside us.

1. What I did today: _____

_____

_____

How it made me feel: _____

_____

_____

2. What I did today: _____

_____

_____

How it made me feel: _____

_____

_____

3. What I did today: _____

_____

_____

How it made me feel: _____

_____

_____

4. What I did today: _____

_____

_____

How it made me feel: _____

_____

_____

5. What I did today: _____

_____

_____

How it made me feel: _____

_____

_____

6. What I did today: _____

_____

_____

How it made me feel: _____

_____

_____

"I Felt Good About My Body"

It's a lot to ask an overeater to feel good about the image they see in the mirror, but you don't have to wait for your ideal weight to feel good about your body. There are dozens of reasons to appreciate what your body does for you. Every healthy, vital sensation that you feel comes from your body. Even when it protests with discomfort and pain, your body is looking out for you. It works tirelessly to keep every cell alive and balanced.

Write down an occasion when you felt grateful for what your body does and appreciated its incredible intelligence. Don't focus on body image. It's more important to establish a good relationship with your body. So today is about building this relationship, turning your body into a strong ally in your journey to complete well-being.

1. What I did today: _____

_____

_____

How it made me feel: _____

_____

_____

2. What I did today: _____

_____

_____

How it made me feel: _____

_____

_____

3. What I did today: _____

_____

_____

How it made me feel: _____

_____

_____

4. What I did today: _____

_____

_____

How it made me feel: _____

_____

_____

5. What I did today: _____

_____

_____

How it made me feel: _____

_____

_____

6. What I did today: _____

_____

_____

How it made me feel: _____

_____

_____

"I Didn't Substitute Food for Feelings"

In this weight-loss program you will repeatedly run across the difference between being hungry for food and being hungry for something else. That's the foundation of the Chopra Solution. You've learned to pause for a moment before you put any food in your mouth and then to check on how you actually feel. At first it may be hard to tell genuine hunger from its substitutes – the need for comfort or the power of cravings, for example. Hunger in its natural state isn't accompanied by any emotional pressure. There's no desperation behind it, no restlessness or worry. To be hungry is to anticipate the pleasure of eating.

Write down your victory over eating for the wrong reasons. Instead, you used food simply as food, not as a substitute for fulfilling another, hidden need.

1. What I did today: _____

_____

_____

How it made me feel: _____

_____

_____

2. What I did today: _____

_____

_____

How it made me feel: _____

_____

_____

3. What I did today: _____

_____

_____

How it made me feel: _____

_____

_____

4. What I did today: _____

_____

_____

How it made me feel: _____

_____

_____

5. What I did today: _____

_____

_____

How it made me feel: _____

_____

_____

6. What I did today: _____

_____

_____

How it made me feel: _____

_____

_____

3

Your Lifestyle

"I Made My Life Lighter"

"I Made My Life More Energetic"

"I Made My Life More Pure"

"I Made My Life More Balanced"

"I Made My Life Lighter"

Although a small minority of dieters can focus on controlling their eating, for most people such an intense, single-minded focus is impossible to maintain. That's one reason why 98% of dieters can't keep off the weight they lose. The answer is to take a holistic approach so that weight loss becomes just one aspect of making your lifestyle better. The Chopra Solution offers four themes that will change how you live, not just how you eat.

The first theme is "lightness." Write down the ways you followed this theme, taking in all the ways it can be applied. Eating lighter foods and making your meals lighter with smaller portions is a good beginning, but the theme also applies to the following:

Turning a heavy mood into a lighter mood.

Choosing to speak lightly to someone instead of criticizing them.

Being light in how you handle your children or spouse.

Turning a heavy physical feeling into lightness through a little movement, such as stretching or walking.

Choosing fresher foods that make you feel light at meal's end instead of packaged or fast food.

Bringing light to your spirit by experiencing the beauty of Nature, children at play, or a moving poem.

Lightening someone else's burden.

All of these things send a message of lightness to your brain, countering messages that are the opposite of light: dull, heavy, dark, depressed, stagnant, fatigued, etc. The more you are able to "be in the light," the more your brain will adopt this as its default mode. Following through with the theme of "lightness" is an enjoyable, satisfying way to change your story, and when your story changes, your body will automatically follow.

1. What I did today: _____

_____

_____

How it made me feel: _____

_____

_____

2. What I did today: _____

_____

_____

How it made me feel: _____

_____

_____

3. What I did today: _____

_____

_____

How it made me feel: _____

_____

_____

4. What I did today: _____

_____

_____

How it made me feel: _____

_____

_____

5. What I did today: _____

_____

_____

How it made me feel: _____

_____

_____

6. What I did today: _____

_____

_____

How it made me feel: _____

_____

_____

"I Made My Life More Energetic"

The second holistic theme is "energy." As with the theme of "lightness," energy applies to any aspect of your life. It comes into play when you eat to feel energetic physically, making use of food as fuel in the best way possible, through sustained, even energy rather than peaks and valleys.

Write down the ways that you became more energetic through any of the following:

Being enthusiastic in your mood.

Actively participating instead of observing.

Inspiring others to be active and committed.

Taking physical exercise instead of avoiding it.

Moving around at least once an hour (a small step but one that is known to normalize physical functions like blood pressure and heart rate).

Including someone in your activities who would otherwise stand on the sidelines.

Bringing new energy to a project that is losing steam.

Being playful instead of serious.

As with all the themes in this program, a simple way to follow through with "energy" is to avoid its opposite, anything that is tired, uninterested, noncommittal, boring, static, and inert. The more you are able to "feel the energy," the more your brain will adopt this as its default mode. Following through with the theme of "lightness" is an enjoyable, satisfying way to change your story, and when your story changes, your body will automatically follow.

1. What I did today: _____

_____

_____

How it made me feel: _____

_____

_____

2. What I did today: _____

_____

_____

How it made me feel: _____

_____

_____

3. What I did today: _____

_____

_____

How it made me feel: _____

_____

_____

4. What I did today: _____

_____

_____

How it made me feel: _____

_____

_____

5. What I did today: _____

_____

_____

How it made me feel: _____

_____

_____

6. What I did today: _____

_____

_____

How it made me feel: _____

_____

_____

"I Made My Life More Pure"

The next lifestyle theme is "purity," which begins with natural, wholesome food. You are adding to the purity of your life by making sure that you throw out stale food, minimize leftovers, and rid your cupboards of packaged, processed foods. That's only the beginning. The opposite of "pure" is "toxic," so any time you change a toxic situation, toxic emotions, or a toxic relationship, you have profoundly changed the messages being sent to your brain.

Write down anything that contributed to leading a purer life, however you want to interpret it. As a guideline, consider if you are moving toward the following things:

Pure emotions instead of toxic emotions.

Clean food, air, and water.

Eliminating the toxic influence of tobacco, alcohol, and drugs.

The freshness of being in Nature.

The innocence of children.

Taking a fresh perspective instead of following old, outworn beliefs.

Having pure intentions instead of selfish ones.

As with all the themes in the program, the best way to become purer is to avoid the opposite of pure: stale, adulterated, contaminated, polluted, etc. Purity feels clean; its opposite feels soiled. Your mind and body are set up to instinctively tell the difference and to choose purity whenever possible.

1. What I did today: _____

_____

_____

How it made me feel: _____

_____

_____

2. What I did today: _____

_____

_____

How it made me feel: _____

_____

_____

3. What I did today: _____

_____

_____

How it made me feel: _____

_____

_____

4. What I did today: _____

_____

_____

How it made me feel: _____

_____

_____

5. What I did today: _____

_____

_____

How it made me feel: _____

_____

_____

6. What I did today: _____

_____

_____

How it made me feel: _____

_____

_____

"I Made My Life More Balanced"

The final theme is "balance," which can sound a bit dull but actually holds the magic key. Your body maintains perfect balance as its default setting. This isn't a mechanical kind of balance but one that is very dynamic and alive, known as homeostasis. Homeostasis is like a springboard, ready to launch you into activity in a split second. When you lose homeostasis, your response is less vibrant and dynamic. You become tired and raise your risk of illness. There is nothing more valuable than the natural state of balance that your mind and body were naturally designed for.

In terms of following the theme of balance in your diet, there are some specific dos and don'ts. Write down your success in following them.

Do: • Eat when you are in a balanced emotional state.

• Consume a wide variety of fresh foods.

• Drinking enough water to be well hydrated.

• Get a good night's sleep.

• Eat at regular hours with balanced intervals in between.

• Vary your calorie intake to balance your activity level.

Don't: • Eat the same few foods every day.

• Go on a "mono diet," where one "magic" food dominates your intake.

• Sit down to eat in a bad mood.

• Eat when you are very tired and exhausted.

• Shun one food group all the time, such as whole grains, fresh fruits, and vegetables.

• Let excess fat begin to unbalance your meals.

These tips are just the beginning. You want your brain to get into a mode that is unstressed and relaxed – that's the bigger goal. So write down the ways that you kept yourself in balance. The following list can serve as a guideline:

Being moderate and reasonable with yourself and others.

Lowering your stress level.

Pushing nothing to extremes.

Finding the right level of activity and rest, ignoring neither one.

Bringing harmony to your surroundings.

Checking to make sure you aren't demanding too much or yourself and others.

1. What I did today: _____

_____

_____

How it made me feel: _____

_____

_____

2. What I did today: _____

_____

_____

How it made me feel: _____

_____

_____

3. What I did today: _____

_____

_____

How it made me feel: _____

_____

_____

4. What I did today: _____

_____

_____

How it made me feel: _____

_____

_____

5. What I did today: _____

_____

_____

How it made me feel: _____

_____

_____

6. What I did today: _____

_____

_____

How it made me feel: _____

_____

_____

4

Your Inner Growth

"I Found Inner Fulfillment"

"I Listened to My Inner Guidance"

"I Touched My Soul"

"I Felt Inspired"

"I Found Inner Fulfillment"

The key to success with *What Are You Hungry For?* is to avoid deprivation and seek fulfillment. Dieters know all about deprivation, but they are much less likely to know about fulfillment – they've developed the habit of using food as a substitute for fulfillment in the areas where there is a real need. Fulfillment must match a specific need if you want to break this habit, which means that you need to name your needs and then set out to meet them.

Write down what you did to fulfill a need without turning to eating. Your awareness will tell you what you really want. It will take practice to get past the blocks that keep you from knowing your real needs, but it's worth the effort, since fulfillment really works. To guide you, here are life's basic needs, with an example or two about the kind of action that brings fulfillment to each need.

Need #1: Comfort, security, safety

(Examples: Owning a house, having a trusted partner/spouse, earning a secure income, living in a safe part of town, taking out insurance, saving for retirement.)

Need #2: Love and affection

(Examples: A loving partner/spouse, close friends, a family where affection is open, being appreciated for your good deeds, service, compassion, believing in God's love.)

Need #3: A sense of belonging

(Examples: Being part of a community, joining a cause, being of service, bonding with co-workers, working in a cooperative atmosphere, making connections with close friends, mentoring, finding a confidante.)

Need #4: Accomplishment and achievement

(Examples: Holding a challenging job, rising at work, becoming a leader, gaining the respect of others, beating the competition, handling crises, becoming notable in your field, raising your children well.)

Need #5: Self-esteem

(Examples: Speaking your truth, standing up for yourself, being proud of who you are, appreciating your accomplishments, letting others see who you really are, valuing others as you value yourself, showing dignity.)

Need #6: Creative expression

(Examples: Writing, journaling, having creative hobbies like music, painting, and community theatre, following your curiosity, making new discoveries, exploring a foreign culture, developing healing and therapeutic skills.)

Need #7: Meaning and purpose

(Examples: Spiritual practice, meditation, feeling connected to a higher power, humanitarianism, charity, giving of yourself.)

The Chopra Solution asks you to look at your needs and ask yourself, "What am I hungry for?" As you get into the habit of asking this simple, basic question, you will stop automatically reaching for food as a crutch for true satisfaction. Instead, you will understand what you really need, and then you can find satisfaction where it will be a positive contribution to your well-being.

1. What I did today: _____

_____

_____

How it made me feel: _____

_____

_____

2. What I did today: _____

_____

_____

How it made me feel: _____

_____

_____

3. What I did today: _____

_____

_____

How it made me feel: _____

_____

_____

4. What I did today: _____

_____

_____

How it made me feel: _____

_____

_____

5. What I did today: _____

_____

_____

How it made me feel: _____

_____

_____

6. What I did today: _____

_____

_____

How it made me feel: _____

_____

_____

"I Listened to My Inner Guidance"

Learning what you really need – the thing you are hungry for, here and now – brings you into contact with your inner awareness. The next step is to find fulfillment, so that your needs are met. Many people, not just overeaters, find this step very difficult. They dream of being deeply satisfied and finding well-being, but somehow all they manage to achieve is moderate happiness, the kind that just gets along. The Chopra Solution is about a deeper, more lasting happiness, the kind that allows you to thrive.

Write down an instance where your inner voice showed you a good choice to make or the answer to a problem. It takes attention and trust to connect with your deepest awareness, but that is where answers and solutions come from. You will be able to thrive by listening to your inner guidance and walking the path this guidance opens before you. What does inner guidance feel like?

It brings calmness and settles fear and worry.

Your choices feel good; they satisfy the situation.

You are no longer in doubt.

You are in harmony with other people;.

You meet less resistance and objections.

You are at peace with yourself.

You have a sense of inner knowingness.

Your choices feel right and don't lead to second-guessing.

Your stress level is lowered.

You get the results you want.

These are the clues that you are heeding true inner guidance and not just acting on impulse or out of worry and stress.

1. What I did today: _____

_____

_____

How it made me feel: _____

_____

_____

2. What I did today: _____

_____

_____

How it made me feel: _____

_____

_____

3. What I did today: _____

_____

_____

How it made me feel: _____

_____

_____

4. What I did today: _____

_____

_____

How it made me feel: _____

_____

_____

5. What I did today: _____

_____

_____

How it made me feel: _____

_____

_____

6. What I did today: _____

_____

_____

How it made me feel: _____

_____

_____

"I Touched My Soul"

Everyone has moments of sheer joy and exaltation. These are the peak moments in life, when you feel free and fulfilled. Your own being is a source of fulfillment. These experiences are a sure sign that you are connected to your very source. The word that most people accept for this source is the soul, but you can substitute other terms that don't have religious connotations, such as your true self or your higher self.

Write down an experience of touching your soul. You can be the judge of what this means – everyone's peak experiences are unique. There will always be a sense of going beyond your everyday self and touching deep-seated bliss, peace, insight, and truth. It's important to take note of such experiences, because that's how your brain learns to align with them. The more closely you pay attention, instead of letting the moment slide by, the more likely you will repeat the experience. As with every kind of experience, your brain must be trained to recognize what is happening and adapt to it. Spiritual experiences aren't excluded, so it's extremely valuable to ground your highest moments in physical reality.

1. What I did today: _____

_____

_____

How it made me feel: _____

_____

_____

2. What I did today: _____

_____

_____

How it made me feel: _____

_____

_____

3. What I did today: _____

_____

_____

How it made me feel: _____

_____

_____

4. What I did today: _____

_____

_____

How it made me feel: _____

_____

_____

5. What I did today: _____

_____

_____

How it made me feel: _____

_____

_____

6. What I did today: _____

_____

_____

How it made me feel: _____

_____

_____

"I Felt Inspired"

The best motivation is inspiration. That's one of the key messages in *What Are You Hungry For?* Your aim is to reach your ideal weight and maintain it from now on. If you try to motivate yourself with constant reminders, calorie counting, self-discipline, and virtuous denial, there isn't much likelihood that you will succeed. Motivation imposes a strain; eventually it wears out. Inspiration, on the other hand, is endlessly renewable because it feels good – the pleasure of feeling inspired makes you want even more.

Write down a moment of inspiration that uplifted you today. Only you can know what inspires you. The general areas of inspiration are music, painting, love, generosity, kindness, natural beauty, poetry, and spiritual literature – exposing yourself to these things opens the way for feeling inspired. In other words, you don't have to wait passively for a bolt from the blue. Your brain is an exquisite instrument for registering joy, bliss, and a profound appreciation for truth and beauty. That's what inspiration is all about. You may find it in the face of a child or a touching human-interest story on the evening news. The real point is to realize that you were designed to be inspired; the choice to seek inspiration is entirely yours.

1. What I did today: _____

_____

_____

How it made me feel: _____

_____

_____

2. What I did today: _____

_____

_____

How it made me feel: _____

_____

_____

3. What I did today: _____

_____

_____

How it made me feel: _____

_____

_____

4. What I did today: _____

_____

_____

How it made me feel: _____

_____

_____

5. What I did today: _____

_____

_____

How it made me feel: _____

_____

_____

6. What I did today: _____

_____

_____

How it made me feel: _____

_____

_____

_____